HISTORY & GEOGRAPHY 206
A JAPANESE FAMILY

CONTENTS

Author: Cynthia P. Dugan

Editor In Chief: Richard W Wheeler, M.A.Ed.

Editor: Janet Monseu

Consulting Editor: Howard Stitt, Th.M., Ed.D.

Revision Editor: Alan Christopherson, M.S.

Alpha Omega Publications®

804 N. 2nd Ave. E., Rock Rapids, IA 51246-1759

Learn with our friends:

When you see me, I will help your teacher explain the exciting things you are expected to do.

When you do actions with me, you will learn how to write, draw, match words, read, and much more.

You and I will learn about matching words, listening, drawing, and other fun things in your lessons.

Follow me and I will show you new, exciting truths, that will help you learn and understand what you study. Let's learn!

A JAPANESE FAMILY

People in America live in families.
People in Japan live in families.
All over the world people live in families.
God wants people in families to love each other.
They show their love by helping each other.
Print what you do to help your family.

People in families work.
They work to get things they need.
All families need food, water
clothes, and homes.
Families work to get things they want.
Families want different things.
Print something your family wants.

People in families teach each other.
Mothers and fathers teach their children.
They teach them how to eat.
They teach them how to dress.
They teach them how to take care of themselves.

Print the name of someone
who teaches you.

In this LIFEPAC, you will learn about families that live in Japan. You will learn how families in Japan help each other. You will find out what children learn in school. You will learn how families in Japan have fun together.

Objectives

Read these objectives. They will tell you what you will be able to do when you have finished this LIFEPAC.

1. You will be able to tell about the kind of work Japanese people do.

2. You will be able to tell some things that make the Japanese family like an American family.

3. You will be able to tell about some things that make the Japanese family different from an American family.

4. You will be able to find Japan on a world map or globe.

5. You will be able to tell one thing about the land in Japan.

6. You will know that all of God's people all over the world are in God's family.

NEW WORDS

arithmetic (a rith me tic). Learning to add and subtract with numbers.

arrange (ar range). To put into some kind of order.

bamboo (bam boo). A plant people use to make things.

bush. A small plant.

caterpillar (cat er pil lar). The worm part of the life of a moth or butterfly.

cocoon (co coon). A silky case caterpillars spin around themselves.

cushion (cush ion). A pillow to sit on.

emperor (em per or). The leader of Japan.

factory (fac tor y). A place where people work together to make something.

festival (fes ti val). A special day when people plan special things to do.

fishermen (fish er men). Men who catch fish.

geta (ge ta). A shoe made of wood.

island (is land). Land with water all around it.

kimono (kē mō`nō) or (ke mo' no). A loose robe.

lantern (lan tern). A light.

machine (ma chine). Something that helps people work or make things.

miso (mē' sō). A soup.

mulberry (mul ber ry). A small fruit that grows on a tree.

nori (nôr 'ē). Seaweed that can be eaten

oyster (oys ter). A fish with a shell.

paddy (pad dy). A field covered with water.

pearl. Something an oyster grows inside its shell.

plow. To dig up the soil.

poem (po em). Words written in lines that often rhyme.

porch. Front part of a house.

rice. A plant with white seeds that can be eaten.

seacoast (sea coast). Land near the sea.

shelf. A place to put things.

silk. A smooth cloth.

sneakers (sneak ers). Soft shoes.

tatami (tô tô' me). Mats that cover the floor.

vegetables (ve ge ta bles). Food.

village (vil lage). A very small town.

whale. An animal that lives in the sea.

These words will appear in **boldface** (darker print) the first time they are used.

I. THE COUNTRY OF JAPAN

Japan is a country in the world. Japan is a small country, but many people live there. The people of Japan love their country. In this part of your LIFEPAC, you will learn some things about Japan.

WORDS TO STUDY

bush		A small plant.
factory	(fac tor y)	A place where people work together to make something.
fishermen	(fish er men)	Men who catch fish.
island	(is land).	Land with water all around it.
machine	(ma chine)	Something that helps people work or make things.
paddy	(pad dy)	A field covered with water.
plow		To dig up the soil.
rice		A plant with white seeds that can be eaten.
seacoast	(sea coast)	Land near the sea.
vegetables	(ve ge ta bles)	Food.
village	(vil lage)	A very small town.
whale		An animal that lives in the sea.

SPECIAL WORD

Tokyo (t ō′ kē ō′)

Ask your teacher to say these words with you.

Teacher Check _____
                Initial   Date

page 5 (five)

PEOPLE IN JAPAN FARM

Many mountains are in Japan. Only a little flat land is left for farms. Farms in Japan are small. Some farms are on the sides of mountains. Big machines are not used on the small farms.

Many farmers in Japan grow rice. They plant a lot of rice. They plant rice because families in Japan like to eat rice. They like to eat rice at every meal.

Rice farmers plow the soil. They plant rice seeds in the soil.

The rice plants begin to grow in small fields. The farmers move the little rice plants to a big field. They plant them in a field that is covered with water.

They plant the little plants in the **paddy**.
The rice will grow in the paddy.
Everyone in the family helps.

Everyone in the family helps.

Many farmers in Japan grow tea.
Families in Japan like to drink hot tea with
their meals. Tea leaves grow on a **bush**.
Farmers plant tea bushes close together.
The workers pick the green tea leaves. They
put the leaves in big baskets.

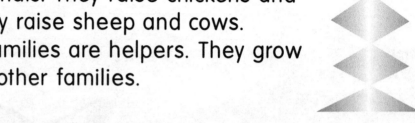

Some farmers in Japan grow **vegetables** and fruit. A few farmers raise animals. They raise chickens and pigs. They raise sheep and cows.

Farm families are helpers. They grow food for other families.

• •

Do these activities.

1.1   Ask someone to help you find Japan on a world map or a globe.

Teacher Check _____
                    Initial   Date

1.2   Print the word Japan.

_____

- -

_____

Read the key words.

1.3   Listen to the ow and ou sounds.
        1. row   2. now   3. ours

Write the number that tells the sound you hear by each of these words.

count   _____   snow   _____
plow   _____   cow   _____
grow   _____   crow   _____
ground _____

Use the same words to finish these sentences.

1.4   The _____ gives us milk.

1.5   The _____ is cold and white.

1.6   Rice needs a lot of water to _____ .

1.7   The farmer will _____ the soil before he plants the seeds.

PEOPLE IN JAPAN FISH

Japan is an **island** country. The sea is all around Japan. The people eat many things that grow in the sea.

Some families live near the **seacoast**. They live in fishing **villages**.

Some people are **fishermen**. Fishermen work on big ships. Fishermen work on little boats. Fishermen catch fish for the people to eat. Some people sell the fish. All the people in the fishing villages are helpers.

Small boats sail around the islands of Japan. They stop near the seacoast. Some people clean the boats.

Fishermen use strong poles and strong lines to catch big fish. Fishermen use nets to catch small fish.

Fish

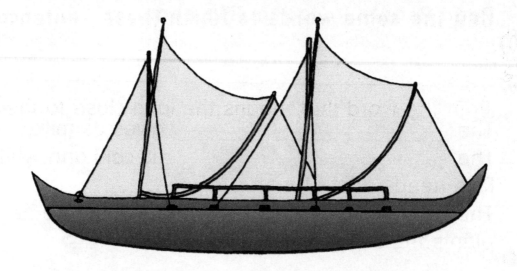

Some fishermen work on big ships. They sail on the sea. Sometimes they catch **whales**. The whale meat is good to eat. Whale oil is used to make soap. Whale oil is used to help plants grow on the farms. Each whale is worth a lot of money.

People of Japan like to eat seaweed. Workers go into the water to find seaweed. Seaweed is dried to eat for breakfast. Seaweed is boiled in good soup. Seaweed can be ground like pepper. Sometimes people wrap seaweed around rice balls. Some people eat seaweed and rice balls for lunch.

Read <u>People in Japan Fish</u> again.

1.8   Print the word that means the land close to the sea.

_____

- -

_____

Do these activities.

1.9   Start with the letter A, follow the letters in order, draw a straight line from dot to dot.

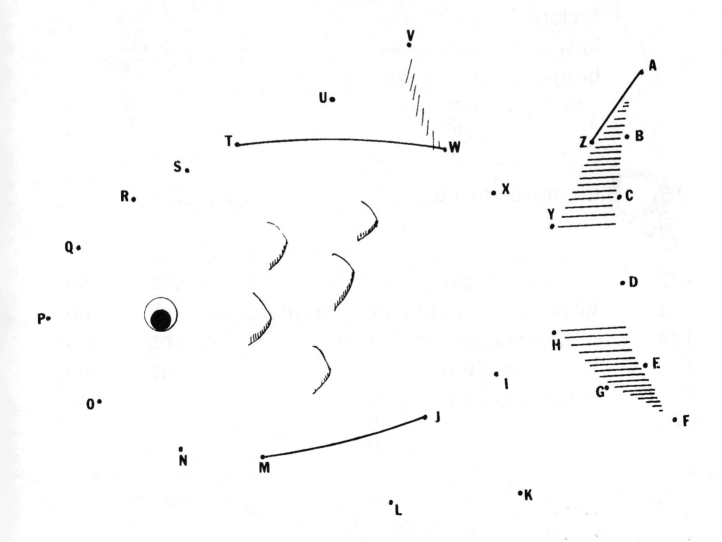

1.10   Print the name of the kind of food in the dot to dot.

_____

- -

_____

Write these new words.

1.11   When a word ends with y, take off the y before you add -ies.

root word	add this	Write the new word.
city	+ -ies	_____
factory	+ -ies	_____
lady	+ -ies	_____
baby	+ -ies	_____
cherry	+ -ies	_____

Circle yes **or** no.

1.12	Japan is an island.	yes	no
1.13	All people in Japan are fishermen.	yes	no
1.14	Whale meat is good to eat.	yes	no
1.15	Soap is made from rice.	yes	no
1.16	Seaweed makes good soup.	yes	no

PEOPLE IN JAPAN LIVE IN CITIES

Many people in Japan live in cities. Tokyo is the biggest city in Japan. Tokyo is also the biggest city in the world.

Busy streets are in Tokyo. Big stores and small shops are in Tokyo. Parks and **factories** are in Tokyo.

Many families live in Tokyo. They work in stores. They work in factories. Factory workers make many things. They make some things we use in America. Factory workers help families.

Some workers do not live in the city. Some people drive to work in the city. Some people take the bus to work. Many people take the train to work.

The fastest train in the world is in Japan. Many people ride on this train.

Tokyo is not the only city in Japan. In each city, families have many things to do. In each city, families have many things to see. Families live close together in the city. They live in apartment houses and they have many neighbors.

- -

 Circle three (3) things you can see in the city.

1.17   busy streets   dragon   tea bushes
        a rice paddy   cornfield   apartment houses
        neighbors

**Unscramble these words to make a sentence.
Write the sentence on the lines.**

1.18   cities. in live people Many Japan in

_____

- -

_____

- -

_____

Do these activities.

1.19   Find out if you have anything in your home that was
made by factory workers in Japan. Write the name
here.

_____

- -

_____

1.20   Print the name of the city that is the biggest city in
the world.

_____

- -

_____

1.21   Print the name of a large city in your country.

_____

- -

_____

For this Self Test, study what you have read and done. The Self Test will check what you remember.

SELF TEST 1

Circle yes **or** no.

1.01	All people need water.	yes	no
1.02	All people need cars.	yes	no
1.03	Japan is in America.	yes	no
1.04	Farms in Japan are small.	yes	no
1.05	Tokyo is a small town.	yes	no
1.06	Fishermen grow corn.	yes	no
1.07	Rice grows in a paddy.	yes	no

Circle two (2) **things that all people need.**

1.08   food   toys   pets   clothes

Circle the name of one food people in Japan eat that most Americans do not eat.

1.09   rice   apples   eggs   seaweed

Print the right word in the sentence.

1.010   Japan is a small _____ .
            city   country   farm

1.011   People in Japan eat _____ at every meal.
            potatoes   meat   rice

1.012   A hot drink that many people in Japan like is

_____ .

milk   coffee   tea

1.013   Some farms in Japan are on the sides of _____

_____ .

mountains   boats   flowers

1.014   A large city in Japan is _____ .

New York   Ohio   Tokyo

1.015   Fish comes from the _____ .

mountain   sea   ground

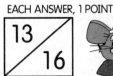

EACH ANSWER, 1 POINT

13	
	16

Teacher Check _____

Initial   Date

My Score

II. A FAMILY AT SCHOOL AND WORK

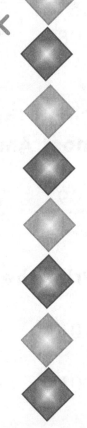

Next, you will read about a family in Japan. The family lives in the city of Nara, Japan.

In the family are twins. The twins are eight years old. The twins' names are Takiko and Tatuso.

The twins have a big sister. Her name is Yoshi.

The twins have a baby brother. His name is Jiro.

The children live with their mother and father. Their grandmother and grandfather live with them, too.

All of God's people in every country are in God's family. God is our heavenly Father. God takes care of us. God gives us families to help take care of us.

WORDS TO STUDY

arithmetic	(a rith me tic)	Learning to add and subtract with numbers.
bamboo	(bam boo)	A plant people use to make things.
caterpillar	(cat er pil lar)	The worm part of the life of a moth or butterfly.
cocoon	(co coon)	A silky case caterpillars spin around themselves.
cushion	(cush ion)	A pillow to sit on.
emperor	(em per or)	The leader of Japan.
geta	(ge ta)	A shoe made of wood.
kimono	(ki mo no)	A loose robe.
miso	(mi so)	A soup.
mulberry	(mul ber ry)	A small fruit that grows on a tree.
nori	(no ri)	Seaweed that can be eaten.

oyster	(oys ter)	A fish with a shell.
pearl		Something an oyster grows inside its shell.
poem	(po em)	Words written in lines that often rhyme.
porch		Front part of a house.
shelf		A place to put things.
silk		A smooth cloth.
sneakers	(sneak ers)	Soft shoes.
tatami	(ta ta mi)	Mats that cover the floor.

SPECIAL WORDS

Fujiyama	Matsuo	Shikoku
Hokkaido	Nara	Takiko
Honshu	Ohayo	Tanaka
Jiro	Osaka	Tatuso
Kyushu	Sayonara	Yoshi

Ask your teacher to say these words with you.

 Teacher Check _____

Initial   Date

THE TWINS HELP AT HOME

Takiko woke up early. She thought about the new day. Today was the last day of school. It was the last day before the New Year.

Takiko was happy. She was happy that the New Year was coming soon.

She was happy to have a new **kimono**. She was happy about the rice cakes her mother made for the New Year's dinner.

Takiko got out of her bed. She went into the kitchen where Mother was busy cooking breakfast. The rice and the fish were ready to eat. The **nori** was also ready.

"Ohayo, good morning," said Takiko. She ate a little piece of seaweed.

"Ohayo," said Takiko's mother. "Go wake up your sleepy brother. We will all eat together."

Takiko ran back to the room.

Tatuso is Takiko's brother. Tatuso was still sleeping. He was in his bed on the floor.

"Wake up, Tatuso," Takiko said.

Tatuso opened his eyes. He did not get up. He was sleepy.

"Wake up, wake up," Takiko said again. Soon Tatuso woke up. He got out of bed.

Then the twins helped each other. They got the room ready for the day. They folded the bedcovers. They put the bedcovers away in the cupboard.

Soon the room was almost ready. Only one bed was left on the floor. Baby Jiro was still asleep in his bed.

ふ
と
ん

Bed

The twins were good workers. They brushed their teeth. They washed their faces. They found their school clothes and got dressed. They were very quiet. They did not wake the baby.

Soon breakfast was ready. The twins sat near the table. The table was very low. No one sat on a chair. Everyone sat on a **cushion**.

Before the family began to eat, the mother and father and children bowed their heads. They gave thanks for the new day. They gave thanks for the good food they had to eat. They gave thanks to God, their heavenly Father.

Do these activities.

2.1   Print the name of the city where the twins live.

_____

- -

_____

2.2   Print the word that means good morning.

_____

- -

_____

Fill in the number word to finish the sentences.

2.3   Takiko and Tatuso are _____ years old.

2.4   In the twins' family are _____ people.

Do this reading activity.
Remember: ay at the end of a word has the long /ā/ sound.
ae sometimes has the long /ā/ sound.
ei, eigh, and ey sometimes have the long /ā/ sound.

2.5   Circle all the words with a long /ā/ sound.

say	day	thanks	make
Japan	eat	break	stay
afraid	eye	neighbor	bear
pail	happy	eight	

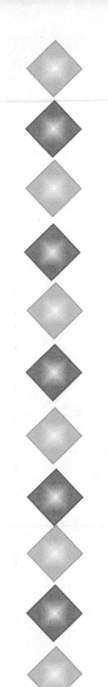

After breakfast Father leaves for work. As Father leaves, the children say "Sayonara."

"Sayonara," says their father. "See you again."

Mr. Tanaka does not have a car. He does not need a car to get to work. A fast train takes him to the city where he works. Each day when the train stops, Mr. Tanaka gets off. He walks with many people. They cross busy streets. They walk over bridges to get to work.

Mr. Tanaka works in Osaka. Osaka is a big city in Japan. Osaka is near the sea. Many people work in Osaka. Some people build ships. Some people make cotton cloth. Some people work with clay. They make pretty bowls. Some people make parts for cars.

Mr. Tanaka works in a car factory. Many people work in the same factory, but they do different things. Some people make the car parts. Some people put the parts together. Some people see if the new car works.

Mr. Tanaka helps the factory owners. He tells them how many cars they have sold. He tells them how much money they have.

HISTORY & GEOGRAPHY

206

LIFEPAC TEST

18 / 22

HISTORY AND GEOGRAPHY 206: LIFEPAC TEST

EACH ANSWER, 1 POINT

Circle yes **or** no.

1.	People in Japan eat rice.	yes	no
2.	The land in Japan is very flat.	yes	no
3.	Japan has many miles of seacoast.	yes	no
4.	Japanese workers use big machines to help on the farms.	yes	no
5.	People in Japan like to eat fish.	yes	no
6.	Japanese picture writing is hard to learn.	yes	no
7.	Japan is an island country.	yes	no

Cross out the sentence that is wrong.

8.   Fishermen are helpers in Japan.
       Farmers are helpers in Japan.
       Letter Carriers are not helpers in Japan.

Circle the right words.

9.   Circle **two** things factory workers make in Japan.

milk	rice	ships
cars	tea	seaweed

10.   Circle **four** things that all people need.

clothes	flowers	water	cars
food	television	homes	toys

1 (one)

11. Circle **two** words that tell about Japan.

mountains   islands   big   flat

12. Circle **two** cities in Japan.

Sayonara   Osaka   Ohayo   Tokyo

Print the right word in the sentence.

13. A Japanese home has _____ mats on the floor.

rugs   bricks   tatami

14. People in Japan can wear a _____ .

osaka   kimono   kite

15. A very small town is a _____ .

village   city   country

16. Many people in Japan _____ when they say "hello."

wave   bow   shake

NOTES

Print some Japanese words.

2.6

English Word	Japanese Word	Print the New Word
Father	Otō-san	_____
Mother	Okā-san	_____
Grandfather	Ojii-san	_____
Grandmother	Obā-san	_____

Circle yes **or** no.

2.7	Sayonara means "Hello."	yes	no
2.8	Mr. Tanaka works in Osaka.	yes	no
2.9	Osaka is a big city.	yes	no
2.10	Cars are made in factories.	yes	no

- -

THE TWINS WALK TO SCHOOL

After Father left for work, it was time for the twins to go to school. They put their books and papers into a book bag. They carried the book bag on their backs. Takiko gave her mother a hug and a kiss before she left. Tatuso did not kiss his mother. Tatuso bowed to his mother.

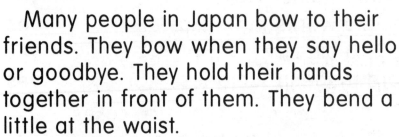

Many people in Japan bow to their friends. They bow when they say hello or goodbye. They hold their hands together in front of them. They bend a little at the waist.

The twins found their outside shoes and put them on. They were ready for school. Mother waved to them as they walked down the street.

All the houses on the street are wood. Most people do not paint their houses. They do not paint over the pretty wood.

All the houses have two floors. All the houses have a **porch**. People leave their outside shoes on the porch.

The twins stopped at the end of the block. They stopped at the busy street. They saw stores that sold many things.

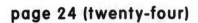

The twins saw people hurrying to work. Some people wear dresses or suits. Some wear kimonos and getas. Takiko liked to hear the sound of wood getas on the sidewalk. Click, clack, click, clack go the getas.

Every morning the twins stopped in front of a big apartment house. They waited outside for Takiko's best friend, Matsuo. Soon Matsuo would come out. Matsuo's mother would come out, too.

Matsuo's mother worked in the city. She worked in a factory. Every morning Matsuo's mother walked with the children on her way to the bus stop.

The girls talked about the new kimonos they will wear on New Year's Day. They talked about the rice cakes they will eat. They talked about the fun they will have with their families.

When the children got to school, they took off their shoes. They put on sneakers. All the children took off their outside shoes. They put their shoes on a shelf. Then they went inside the classroom.

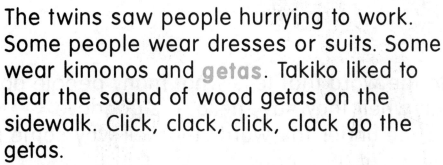

Geta

Do these activities.

2.11   Write the word that tells what many people do in Japan when they say "hello" or "goodbye." _____

2.12   Put a line under the words that tell why some people do not paint their house.

          it is too hot
          it is too cold
          the wood is pretty
          they do not have paint

Where did the children leave their outside shoes?

2.13   at home   _____

2.14   at school   _____

Circle the word that tells what special cakes the children will eat on New Year's Day.

2.15   rice   birthday   pan

Write the right word in each sentence.

2.16   Matsuo was _____ best friend.
        Tatsuo's   Yoshi's   Takiko's

2.17   When the children got to school, they put on

    _____ .

    shoes   sneakers   getas

THE TWINS LEARN AT SCHOOL

に

ぽ

ん

Japan

In Japan children learn to read and write. They learn to do **arithmetic**. They learn many things that American children learn.

Some things they learn are different. Children in Japan learn to do picture writing. Picture writing is not easy to learn. The children work and write many hours so they can do the picture writing. They work many hours so they can read the picture writing.

と

う

き

ょ

う

Tokyo

おとこ のこ

This writing says a boy.

おんな のこ

This writing says a girl.

Sometimes the children in Tatuso's class talk about Japan. "The names of the big islands are Hokkaido, Honshu, Shikoku, and Kyushu," Tatuso says as he points to the map.

"Honshu is the biggest island. Honshu Island has big cities. Tokyo is a city on Honshu. Nara is a city on Honshu," says Takiko.

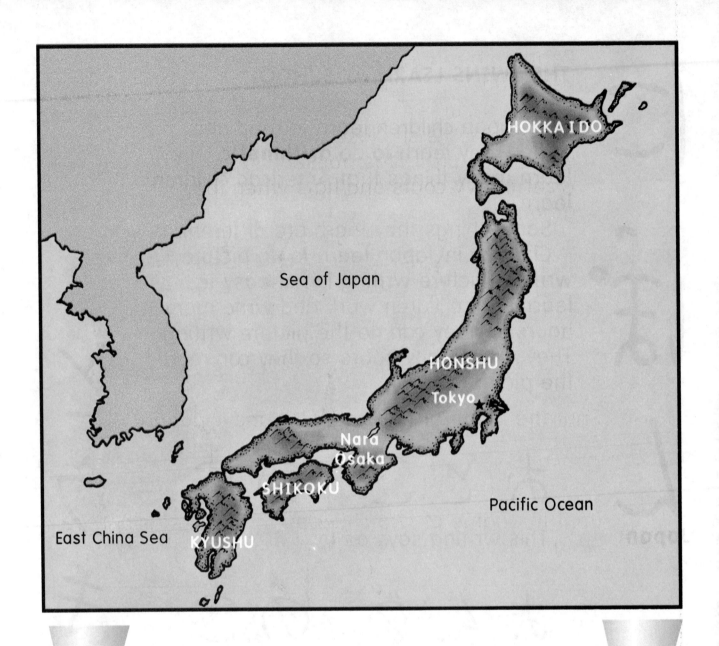

"Many mountains are on Honshu. The name of one mountain is Fujiyama. We call this mountain Mount Fuji. Mount Fuji is very tall. Mount Fuji is very pretty."

" In the summer people climb to the top of this mountain," says another girl.

The children learn that summer in Japan is hot. People go to the seaside.

People go to the mountains. They go to keep cool.

Wintertime is cold. Snow falls in some places. People sit close to the heater when they are in the house. People wear heavy coats and hats when they go outside.

Do these activities.

2.18   Print the name of the biggest island in Japan.

_____

- -

_____

2.19   Print the name of two cities on the biggest island in Japan.

_____   _____

THE TWINS LEARN MORE ABOUT JAPAN

In the afternoon at school, Takiko learns about the **silk caterpillar**. She learns that farmers feed silk caterpillars. They feed them **mulberry** leaves every day. The caterpillars eat and eat. They eat until it is time to make a **cocoon**.

The farmer sells the cocoons to a silk factory. The factory makes silk cloth. Some silk cloth is used for kimonos. Some women in America wear silk dresses.

The children also learn about the **pearl oyster**. The children learn that pearls are found inside some oysters. They learn that some pearls are smooth and round. People in Japan think pearls are pretty. People in America think pearls are pretty, too. Many people like to wear pearls. They wear pearl rings. They wear pearl necklaces.

Once the teacher told the children about a plant called **bamboo**. Bamboo grows very fast in Japan. It grows tall like a tree, but bamboo is not a tree. Bamboo is used for many things. Bamboo is used to make fishing poles, pots, bowls, fans, and umbrellas. People in Japan use bamboo to build houses.

Make a paper mountain.

2.20 You will need a piece of notebook paper. Fold on the dots. Follow the arrows.

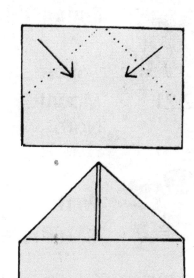

1. Fold the top corners down. The sides will meet in a straight line.

2. Fold the bottom up to the fold line. Fold in half again.

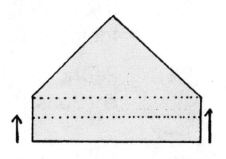

3. Turn the paper over and fold down the triangle on top.

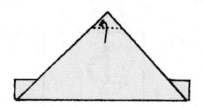

4. Color the mountain. Make it look like snow at the top.

Finish this sentence.

2.21 Mount _____ is a tall mountain in Japan.
     Nara   Fuji   Tokyo

Write in the word that will finish the sentence.

2.22 Silk caterpillars eat mulberry _____ .
     seeds   food   leaves   milk

2.23 Silk cloth is used to make _____ .
     tables   dresses   bowls   fishing poles

2.24 Pearls are found in _____ .
     cocoons   fish   oysters   bamboo

Fill in the letters to name a plant that grows in Japan.

2.25

b		m			o

Sometimes children write **poems** in school. They write poems for the **emperor** of Japan. Each year the emperor of Japan asks the children to write a poem. Many children send a poem to the emperor. He chooses a poem he likes best.

This is Tatuso's poem:

The New Year coming
Bringing food, fun, and presents
makes us all happy.

This is Matsuo's poem:

Pretty, yellow, long.
A kimono of my own.
Makes me feel all grown.

This is Takiko's poem:

The geta, a shoe.
Makes a funny, funny noise
But a noise I like.

 Circle the right word.

2.26   Tatuso's poem was about _____ .
        New Year   shoes   kimonos

2.27   The children wrote poems for _____ .
        mother   father   the emperor

Do this activity.

2.28   Print the poem you like best.

_____

_____

_____

 Teacher Check _____

MOTHER WORKS AT HOME

While their children are away, Japanese mothers are busy.

Many mothers work at home. Takiko's mother works at home.

Today is a special day. Takiko's mother has a lot to do in the house. She must get ready for the New Year.

This morning the children helped Mother. They helped by putting the bedclothes away. They helped by letting the baby sleep.

Now Grandmother will help. She will watch baby Jiro. She will feed the baby. She will keep him happy while Mother works. Mother makes some **miso** for supper.

Mother wants the house clean for the New Year. She wants the clothes washed and the food cooked. She does not want to work on New Year's Day.

Mother sweeps the **tatami** mats. The tatami mats are all over the house. The tatami mats cover the floor. The tatami are not very dirty. They are not very dirty because no one wears shoes when they step on the tatami. Everyone leaves his or her shoes outside.

Mother hears the mailman. She goes to the mailbox. Inside she finds many cards. The cards are from friends. They are Happy New Year cards. Mother puts the cards on a shelf. She wants everyone to see the cards from their friends.

When Mother shops, she buys many things. Color the pictures of the foods Mother buys.

Colors to use: 1. red 2. yellow 3. orange 4. light green 5. purple 6. brown 7. gray 8. white

2.29

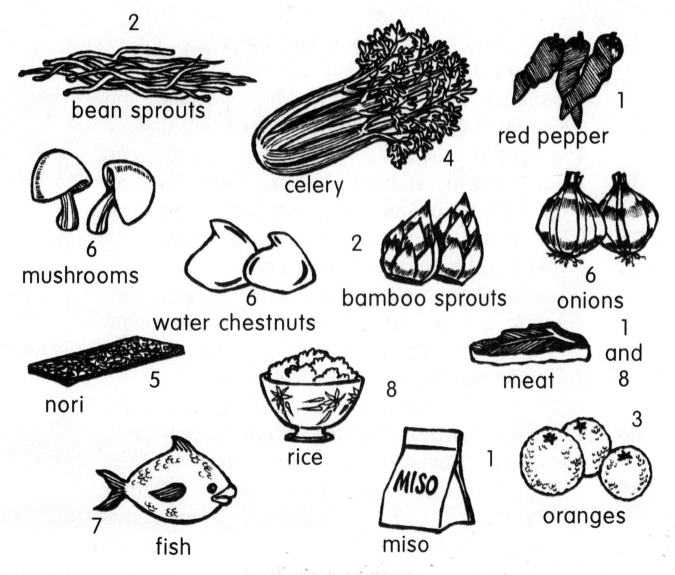

2

bean sprouts

celery

1

red pepper

4

6

mushrooms

6

water chestnuts

2

bamboo sprouts

6

onions

5

nori

8

rice

meat

1 and 8

1

miso

3

oranges

7

fish

Circle two (2) things Mother does.

2.30   sweeps tatami   works in factory   cooks food

Study what you have read and done for this Self Test. This Self Test will check what you remember of this part and other parts you have read.

SELF TEST 2

Circle yes **or** no.

2.01	The family in Japan had eggs and bacon for breakfast.	yes	no
2.02	Osaka is near the sea.	yes	no
2.03	People in Japan shake hands when they say hello.	yes	no
2.04	Some people in Japan live in apartment houses.	yes	no
2.05	Picture writing is easy to learn.	yes	no
2.06	Tokyo is the biggest city in the world.	yes	no
2.07	Japan is a big country.	yes	no

Circle the right words.

2.08   Circle two words that tell about Japan.
          islands   big   flat   small

2.09   Circle two things people do at work in Osaka.
          build ships   grow rice   milk cows
          make parts for cars   catch whales

2.010   Circle the word that tells in which group a kimono belongs.

food   water   clothes   homes

2.011   Circle the words that tell why many people in Japan do not paint their houses.

no paint in Japan
it is too cold
the wood is pretty

2.012   Circle the word that tells where rice grows.
mountain   park   paddy   playground

2.013   Circle the word that tells something fishermen catch.
water   corn   puppies   whales

2.014   Circle the word that tells where many people in Japan live.
parks   cities   mountains   sea

Print the right word in each sentence.

2.015   Before breakfast the family gives thanks to

_____ .

God   Father   Mother

2.016   A tall mountain in Japan is Mount _____ .
Osaka   Fuji   Tokyo

2.017   A hot drink many people in Japan drink is _____ .
         tea   coffee   milk

2.018   At every meal, people in Japan like to eat
         _____ .
         cereal   rice   popcorn

2.019   The family sits on _____ when they eat.
         benches   chairs   cushions

2.020   Mr. Tanaka takes the _____ to work.
         airplane   bus   train

2.021   A Japanese bed is _____ .
         very small   on the floor   very big

2.022   A food many people in Japan eat is _____ .
         ice cream   popcorn   fish

2.023   Tatuso and Takiko are _____ .
         twins   babies   cities

2.024   Some fishing poles are made of _____ .
         bamboo   pine   oak

EACH ANSWER, 1 POINT

19/24

 Teacher Check _____

                    Initial   Date

My Score

III. A FAMILY AT PLAY

Families work together. Families have fun together. God is pleased when families are happy and loving.

WORDS TO STUDY		
arrange	(ar range)	To put into some kind of order.
festival	(fes ti val)	A special day when people plan special things to do.
lantern	(lan tern)	A light.

Ask your teacher to say these words with you.

Teacher Check _____

Initial   Date

CHILDREN HAVE FUN AFTER SCHOOL

Yoshi is the twins' sister. After school Yoshi goes to another class. Many girls go with Yoshi. They go to class to learn about flowers. Yoshi likes this class. She learns how to help at home. She learns how to **arrange** the flowers.

Takiko and Matsuo do not go home after school. Takiko and Matsuo go to a Brownie meeting. They learn to play new games. They learn to sing new songs.

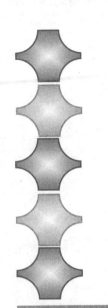

They learn to help at home. They have fun like other Brownies all over the world.

Tatuso does not go home after school. Tatuso goes with his friends. Today Tatuso and his friends go to the playground. They go to play baseball. Many boys in Japan like to play baseball.

Write the word that will finish the sentence.

3.1   Pretty flowers grow in the _____ .
       chair   spring   air   bowl

3.2   Tatuso will _____ the baseball.
       eat   like   throw   send

3.3   Children in Japan go to _____ .
       like   school   bamboo   maple

Do this reading activity.

You will hear people say that Jesus is our Redeemer. They mean that Jesus will help us again and again. The word part re- means again.

3.4   Write the word part re- in front of these words.
       Draw a line to the right words.

       _____ count   to make new again
       _____ build   to build again
       _____ new   to count over

page 40 (forty)

The word part un- means not.

3.5   Write the word part un- in front of these words.
        Draw a line to match the right words.

        _____ cooked   not cut
        _____ cut   not cooked

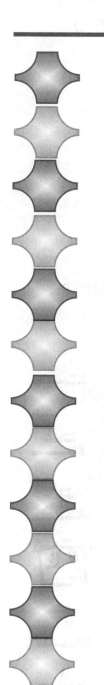

FAMILIES HAVE FUN AT FESTIVALS

Sometimes families in Japan have fun getting ready for festivals.

The Bon Festival is in July. During the Bon Festival people remember their families. They remember everyone in their families. The people light pretty lanterns. They put lanterns near the streets. The pretty lanterns light the way for all the people.

On New Year's Day many people visit their friends. They give gifts to each other. The stores are closed. People dress in their best kimonos. The New Year Festival is a happy time.

On Girl's Day, girls show their dolls to their friends. They do not play with the dolls. They put the dolls on shelves for everyone to see. Friends come to see the dolls. Girls give them tea and rice cakes to eat.

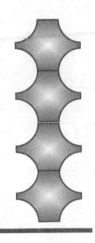

On Boy's Day, many people buy fish kites. They put the kites on long bamboo poles. They fly the fish kites in the wind. The fish kites help the boys remember to be strong and brave.

Draw a line from the festival to the things the people use on that day.

3.6	Girl's Day	fish kites
3.7	Boy's Day	lanterns
3.8	The Bon Festival	dolls
3.9	New Year's Day	gifts

Learn to write Japanese numbers. The Japanese people write with a brush.

3.10   one   _____   一   一

two   _____   二   二

three   _____   三   三

four   _____   四   四

five   _____   五   五

six   _____   六   六

seven   _____   七   七

eight   _____   八   八

nine   _____   九   九

ten   _____   十   十

Study what you have read and done for this last Self test. This Self Test will check what you remember in your studies of all parts in this LIFEPAC. The last Self Test will tell you what parts of the LIFEPAC you need to study again.

SELF TEST 3

Circle yes **or** no.

3.01   A factory worker is a community helper.   yes   no

3.02   Some Japanese girls are Brownies.   yes   no

3.03   In Japan, people wear shoes inside their houses.   yes   no

3.04   Children work many hours to learn picture writing.   yes   no

Circle the right answer.

3.05 Circle the name of the community helper that catches whales.

fisherman doctor farmer

3.06 Circle the name of the community helper that grows food.

fisherman factory worker farmer

3.07 Circle the name of the helper that gets Matsuo's mother to work.

fisherman bus driver factory worker

3.08 Circle the word that tells what many people do in Japan when they say "hello."

wave hide bow

3.09 Circle the word that tells what grows in a paddy.

corn rice tea

3.010 Circle the word that names the largest city in Japan.

Nara Tokyo New York

Print the right word in the sentence.

3.011 In Japan, no one wears shoes when they step on the

_____ .

tatami sidewalk floor

3.012 One game boys like to play in Japan is _____

_____ .

football basketball baseball

3.013   Pearls are found in _____ .

        fish   seaweed   oysters

3.014   On New Year's Day, people in Japan give

       _____ .

        getas   gifts   kites

3.015   On Girl's Day, girls show _____ to their friends.

        dolls   dogs   fish

3.016   Yoshi learned to arrange _____ .

        farms   food   flowers

3.017   Many people in Japan live in _____ .

        mountains   cities   parks

3.018   God wants families to _____ each other.

        like   live   love

EACH ANSWER, 1 POINT

14 / 18

 Teacher Check _____

                       Initial   Date

My Score

Before taking the LIFEPAC Test, you should do these self checks.

1. Did you do good work on your last Self Test?

2. Did you study again those parts of the LIFEPAC you did not remember?

   Check one:　　☐ Yes (good)
   　　　　　　　☐ No (ask your teacher)

3. Do you know all the new words in "Words to Study"?

   Check one:　　☐ Yes (good)
   　　　　　　　☐ No (ask your teacher)